THE

Vintage

COLOURING & CRAFT BOOK

LISA HUGHES

ILLUSTRATED BY
PATRICIA MOFFETT

Waterford City and County
Libraries

CARLTON BOOKS

THIS IS A CARLTON BOOK

Published by Carlton Books Ltd
20 Mortimer Street
London W1T 3JW

Copyright © Carlton Publishing Group
2016

A CIP catalogue for this book is
available from the British Library.

Project editor: Charlotte Selby
Design manager: Lucy Palmer
Layout: Rebecca Wright
Production: Ebyan Egal

ISBN 978-1-78097-811-6

Printed in Slovenia

10 9 8 7 6 5 4 3 2 1

INTRODUCTION

If you've already embraced the colouring craze, you'll know that colouring is a great creative outlet – but what's special about this book is that it features a range of colouring and craft projects for you to colour and cut out, and helps you take your creativity a step further.

To get started, you'll need colouring pens, pencils, and scissors. Other materials and tools are listed, but you'll probably have most of them to hand anyway. If you only need to colour one side of a piece, the instructions will say so and you can choose which side to colour. Otherwise, colour both sides. If you have access to a photocopier or scanner, you can also copy and print the designs for your personal use; alternatively you could trace them using transfer paper or a light box.

I really get great pleasure from making things and I hope you enjoy making these projects as much as I've enjoyed creating them.

Lisa Hughes

THE PALETTES

Here are some colour combinations to inspire your craft projects.

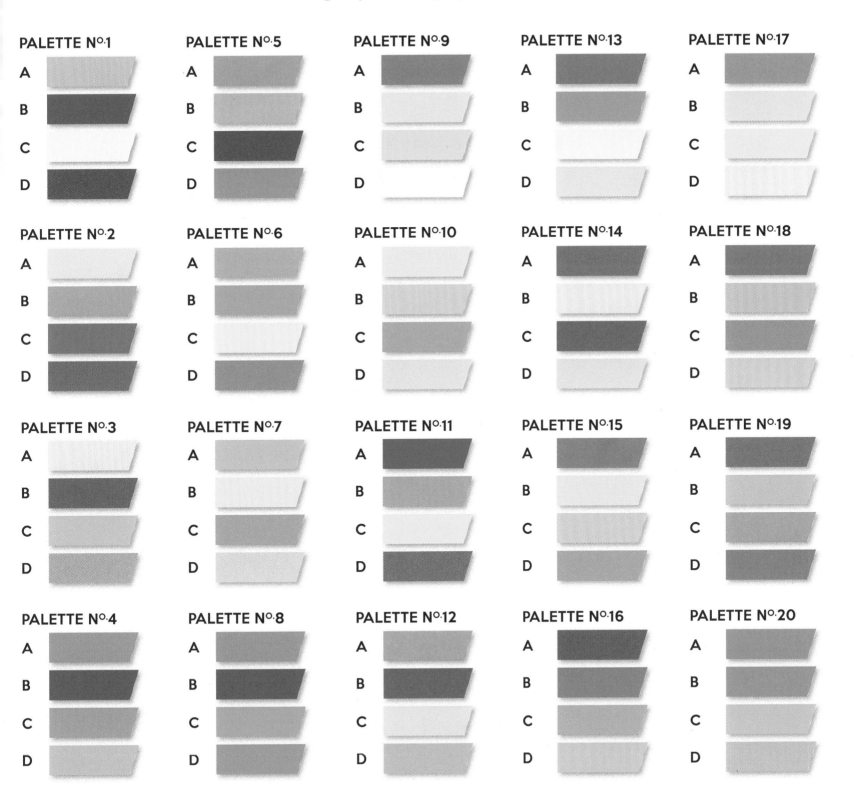

PALETTE N°·1

A
B
C
D

PALETTE N°·5

A
B
C
D

PALETTE N°·9

A
B
C
D

PALETTE N°·13

A
B
C
D

PALETTE N°·17

A
B
C
D

PALETTE N°·2

A
B
C
D

PALETTE N°·6

A
B
C
D

PALETTE N°·10

A
B
C
D

PALETTE N°·14

A
B
C
D

PALETTE N°·18

A
B
C
D

PALETTE N°·3

A
B
C
D

PALETTE N°·7

A
B
C
D

PALETTE N°·11

A
B
C
D

PALETTE N°·15

A
B
C
D

PALETTE N°·19

A
B
C
D

PALETTE N°·4

A
B
C
D

PALETTE N°·8

A
B
C
D

PALETTE N°·12

A
B
C
D

PALETTE N°·16

A
B
C
D

PALETTE N°·20

A
B
C
D

CONTENTS

49 Cocktail Coasters

53 Notebook Cover

57 Cactus

63 Memory Game

67 Light Holder

71 Pendant Box

75 Kitchen Theme Artwork

79 3D Heart Picture

83 Home Sweet Home Picture

87 Christmas Baubles

91 Vintage Alphabet

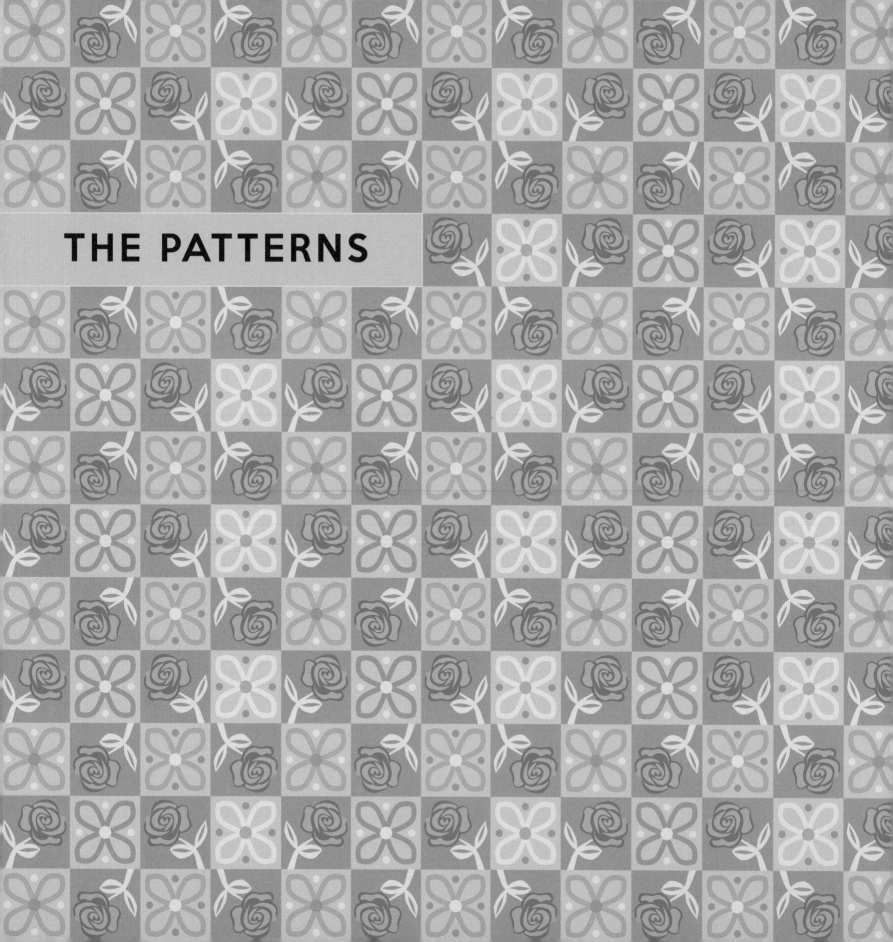

THE PATTERNS

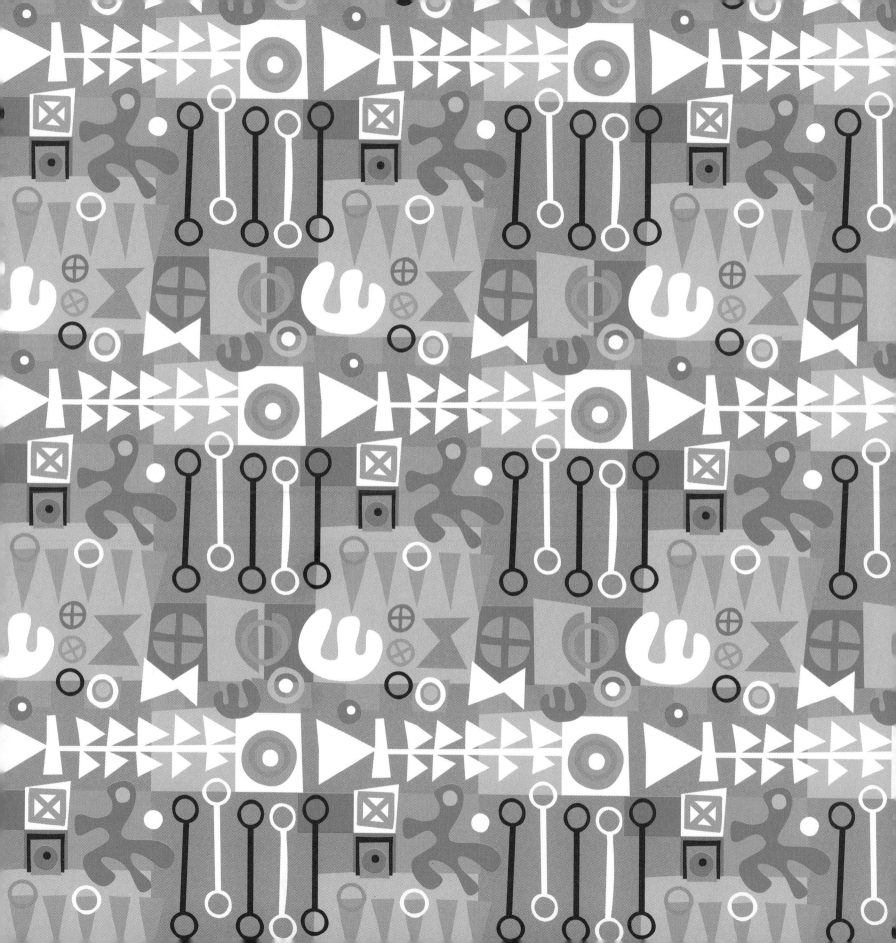

THE PROJECTS

Homemade by

Party Invite Decorations

Throwing a stylish cocktail party? Set the tone with a beautiful handmade invitation. Don't forget to include date, time, place and dress code. Whatever the occasion, these card toppers will help you create an impact.

MATERIALS AND TOOLS

- Craft knife and cutting surface
- Card or A6 card blanks
- Glue or double-sided sticky tape
- Sequins, glitter or ribbon

INSTRUCTIONS

1 Choose your designs, colour them in – you only need to colour one side – and cut them out. For some of the more intricate designs, you may find it easier to rest them on a cutting surface and use a craft knife.

2 Take a card blank – if you're creating your own, measure to fit the envelope, cut and fold the card – and arrange the toppers to your satisfaction.

3 Stick the designs to the cards and embellish with a dusting of glitter, a sprinkling of sequins or a thin ribbon border.

MORE IDEAS AND INFORMATION

• To set off the toppers, try mounting them on a rectangle or oval of coloured paper before you stick them to the card.

• For 3D cards, use double-sided sticky pads to lift the toppers away from the card.

• These toppers are also ideal for making any kind of celebration card.

New Home Cards

Moving into a new home is a cause for celebration, so send a beautiful handmade card to mark the event. Here is a simple but effective project on the new home theme, but the idea can be easily adapted to mark any special occasion.

MATERIALS AND TOOLS

- Small letter stamps and ink pad
- Craft knife, cutting surface and metal ruler
- Coloured card or A6 card blank
- Double-sided sticky pads

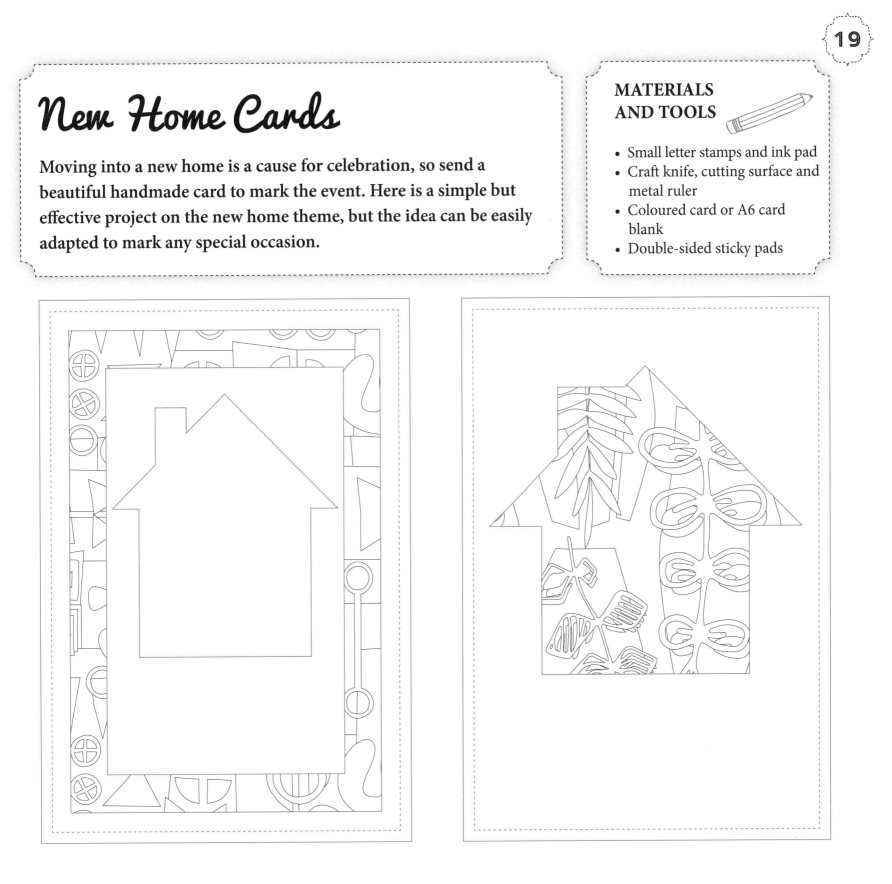

INSTRUCTIONS

1 Colour in the house and frame – you only need to colour one side – and cut out the rectangles they sit in.

2 On the rectangle with the frame, use letter stamps to write a message below the house shape – 'New home' is the obvious one. You could also handwrite this or print it out in your favourite font.

3 Place this rectangle on your cutting surface and use the craft knife to cut out the house shape.

4 Centre the patterned house on the front of your card – there should be a small border all the way round – and stick it down.

5 Using the double-sided sticky pads, stick the rectangle with the house-shaped hole on top. Support it at the corners and the edges of the hole, cutting the pads if necessary.

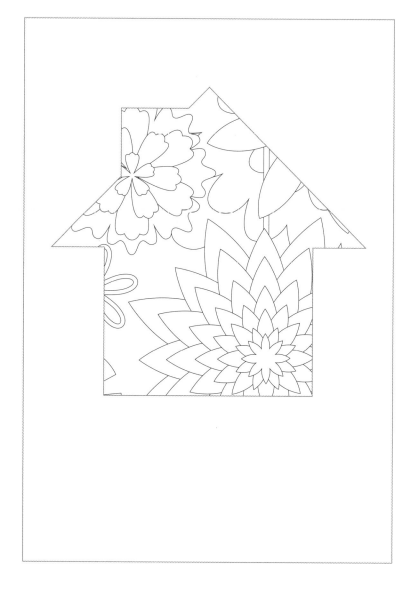

Vintage-themed Gift Tags

A gift tag you've made yourself is the ultimate personal touch. This retro luggage label tag is perfect if you're giving tickets for a surprise trip, holiday accessories or any travel-related present; but if that doesn't fit the bill there are other tags to make here too.

MATERIALS AND TOOLS

- Craft knife and cutting surface
- Glue or double-sided sticky tape
- Clear cellophane or similar
- Narrow ribbon

INSTRUCTIONS

1 Colour in both sides of the large luggage label tag and cut it out. Colour in the luggage label window and card – you only need to colour one side of these – and cut them out.

2 On your cutting surface, using the craft knife, cut out the slot for the ribbon on the large piece.

3 Then cut out the central area of the window piece and stick a small rectangle of cellophane over the back of it.

4 Run glue or tape close the edges of three sides of the window (not the side that will be closest to the ribbon hole) and stick it to the front of the tag, over the blank area.

5 Write the card, slip it into the pocket and add a ribbon.

6 To make the other tags, colour them in, cut them out and thread ribbon through the holes.

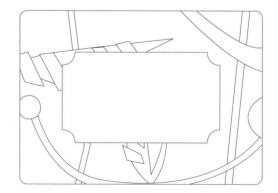

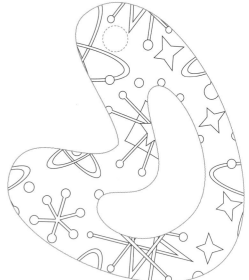

MORE IDEAS

• Plain wrapping paper combined with your own beautifully coloured tag will really give your gift the wow factor.

• The classic atomic 'boomerang'-shaped tag is particularly suitable for a vintage gift.

• Tags like these can also be used to label laundry bags filled with spare bedding or clothes you've put away.

Indoor Bunting

There's just something so cheerful about bunting. Of course, it's often hung in children's bedrooms, but it brightens up a space any day of the week, especially if you pick out the accent colours in your decor. Go on, get out the flags!

MATERIALS AND TOOLS

- 1.3m baker's twine, ribbon or string
- Double-sided sticky tape or glue

INSTRUCTIONS

1 Choose your designs and colour them in. Colour one side if you're hanging the bunting on a wall or both if it's going to go across a room. Cut them out.

2 On a table, stretch out the twine and space the bunting pieces along it evenly – allow about 3cm between each one. Alternate the large and small triangles.

3 Fold over the top edge of each piece of bunting by 1cm. Slip the twine under this flap and stick the flap down, enclosing the twine and holding it in place. Make sure you keep the spacing even.

4 Turn the bunting over and snip away the triangles of excess paper that are visible at the top on both sides of each triangle, but be careful to avoid cutting the twine as well. Hang your bunting.

MORE IDEAS AND INFORMATION

- Use the alphabet on page 91 to spell out a message on your bunting.

- At a festival, bunting is a great way to identify your tent. If you have access to a laminator, you can even waterproof it.

- A miniature version of this bunting makes a lovely card topper.

Butterfly Gift Decoration

If a gift's worth giving, it's worth wrapping beautifully – and this striking folded butterfly decoration will add a touch of class to your presentation. It may look complicated, but follow the step-by-step instructions carefully and you'll find it's actually quite straightforward.

MATERIALS AND TOOLS

- Glue or sticky tape
- Skewer

INSTRUCTIONS

1 Colour the butterfly pieces – you only need to colour one side – and cut them out.

2 Take the large square of paper. With the pattern facing up and starting with one point, make a series of small concertina folds about 0.5cm wide, right down to the triangle's point.

3 Wind one of the thin strips a couple of times around the centre of the folded square and hold it in place with a dab of glue.

4 Take the rectangle with the rounded corners. With the pattern facing up and starting with the long edge, make a series of concertina folds about 0.5cm wide, until you've used all the paper.

5 Put the folded square on top of the rectangle, wind the thin strip from step 3 around both centres and hold it in place with a dab of glue. Trim off the excess. These are the butterfly's wings.

6 Twist the wide strip around the skewer to form a long, thin tube. Hold the end in place with a dab of glue and remove the skewer. Flatten one end and cut it to a point. This is the butterfly's body.

7 With the pattern facing outwards, fold one of the thin strips of paper lengthways and secure with a dab of glue. Fold it in half diagonally to form a V and cut the ends at an angle. These are the butterfly's antennae. Insert them into the flattened end of the body.

8 Take the two remaining thin strips and cut one end of each to a point about 3cm long. These are the butterfly's tail wings. Gently unfold the rounded bottom wings and stick a tapered tail wing to the edge nearest the centre of each of the wings.

9 Stick the body across the middle of the wings, flattening it slightly, and gently spread the wings. Stick the butterfly to your gift.

MORE IDEAS AND INFORMATION

- The butterfly is light, so it can also be Blu-Tacked to the wall.

- Hanging it works well, too, but you need to colour both sides of the wing pieces.

- If you can photocopy the pieces and make several butterflies, they look stunning hung in a group.

Heart Garland

This heart garland is very pretty, and it's also simple and quick to make. Hang it near a window you can open so that on a fine day it will twist and turn in the breeze.

MATERIALS AND TOOLS

- 1.5m cotton thread, baker's twine or thin ribbon
- Invisible tape
- Small bead

INSTRUCTIONS

1 Colour the hearts and circles and cut them out. Lay the shapes out in the order you want to hang them in.

2 Leaving enough thread at the top to hang the garland, run the thread down the middle of the first shape and tape it in place.

3 Repeat this until all shapes are attached to the thread, leaving an even amount of thread between each one.

4 Finish off the garland and weight the bottom by gluing or tying the small bead to the end of the thread. Hang your garland.

MORE IDEAS AND INFORMATION

• If you use thin ribbon instead of thread and close up the spacing between the shapes, this heart garland is great for gift-wrapping.

• A line of heart garlands hung from the underside of the top edge of an old picture frame looks lovely or string a few above your bed in place of a headboard.

• You could also add the 3D hearts on page 79 to your garland.

Standing Birds

There's something very engaging about these quirky paper birds. Perch one on a ledge or let it fly across the mantelpiece. They're chirpy, cheerful and charming. Who could resist?

MATERIALS AND TOOLS

- Sticky tape or glue gun, and glue
- Paperclips

INSTRUCTIONS

1 Colour a bird body – you only need to colour one side – and two matching wings. Draw in eyes on the body. Cut all the pieces out.

2 Make a fold 0.5cm from the straight edge of a wing and glue this to the coloured-in side of the bird body. Bend the wing out from the body, towards you. Do the same with the other wing and bird body.

3 Take two paperclips. Bend the inner ends up and straighten them. These are the legs. Tape or glue-gun them to the undecorated side of one half of the bird body.

4 Glue the two undecorated sides of the bird body together and adjust the legs so that the bird stands.

5 Colour in a strip of grass – you only need to colour one side – and cut it out. Stick bent paperclips to the back so that it stands up. Place it in front of your bird.

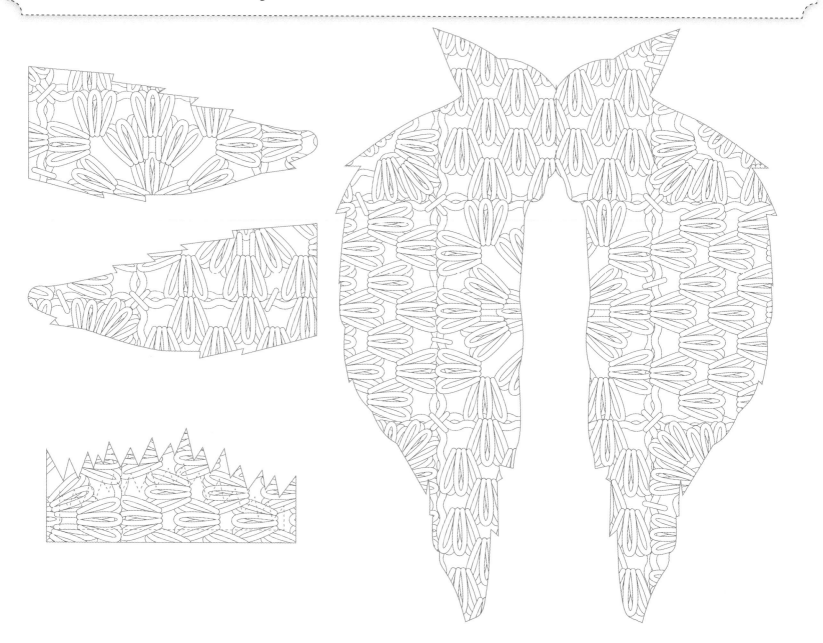

MORE IDEAS AND INFORMATION

• If you have access to a photocopier, make a flock of these birds.

• Tape name cards to their backs for sweet place settings.

• The birds can also be suspended from the ceiling. Find the balancing point in their backs, push a threaded needle through, and hang the birds from the thread.

Jam and Preserve Labels

Strawberry jam, lemon curd, marmalade, pickled onions, chutney, even piccalilli (for those who like it) – choose a label style that suits you or what you've made, or mix it up and decorate each jar differently. Your produce will look so gorgeous you won't want to give it away!

MATERIALS AND TOOLS

- Glue or double-sided sticky tape

Homemade by

INSTRUCTIONS

1 Choose your labels, colour them in – you only need to colour one side – and cut them out.

2 Write the contents and date on the labels.

3 Stick the labels to the jars and lids.

Homemade by

_____

HOMEMADE

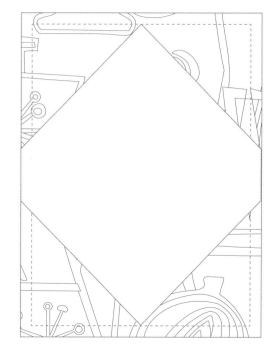

MORE IDEAS AND INFORMATION

• These can also be used for herbs and spices or for labelling any kitchen-storage jars.

• They're also handy for keeping track of the contents of box files and folders.

• Photocopying the labels onto self-adhesive paper before you colour them will mean they're even easier to stick on.

Keepsakes Envelope

A postcard, a handwritten note, a train ticket, a child's drawing, a scrap of fabric – these are the things that trigger happy memories, but all too often they get lost along the way. Keep them safe in one of these keepsakes envelopes.

MATERIALS AND TOOLS

- Glue or double-sided sticky tape
- 2 paper fasteners
- 10cm baker's twine or narrow ribbon

INSTRUCTIONS

1 Colour the front of the square. On the back, only colour the top 3cm. Cut it out.

2 Colour the front of the square with flaps. Only colour the top 3cm of the square itself and don't colour the thin tabs on the bottom and sides, but do colour the top flap. Colour all the back. Cut it out.

3 Push a paper fastener from front to back where marked and open out the arms. Push the other one from back to front through the top flap of the square with flaps where marked and open out the arms. Tie or stick one end of the twine to the head of the fastener in the flap, on the back of the piece.

4 Place the square on top of the square with flaps, front upwards. Fold the bottom and side flaps over and stick them to the top square.

5 Colour the circles, cut them out and stick them on for decoration.

6 Fold over the top flap. Loop the twine around the fasteners in a figure of eight.

MORE IDEAS

• Label your keepsakes envelope with one of the labels on page 41.

• Glue a keepsakes envelope to the inside cover of a photo album and slip loose snaps in there.

• Only hold on to what's really precious and limit yourself to filling just one of these envelopes in a single year.

Cocktail Coasters

To reduce the chance of spills at a smart drinks party or stop cups from leaving ring marks on your coffee table, make these striking coasters. Vintage patterns work beautifully on them – go for a matching set or mix them up.

MATERIALS AND TOOLS

- Cork tile at least 0.5cm thick
- Craft knife, cutting surface and metal ruler
- Glue
- Gloss varnish and brush

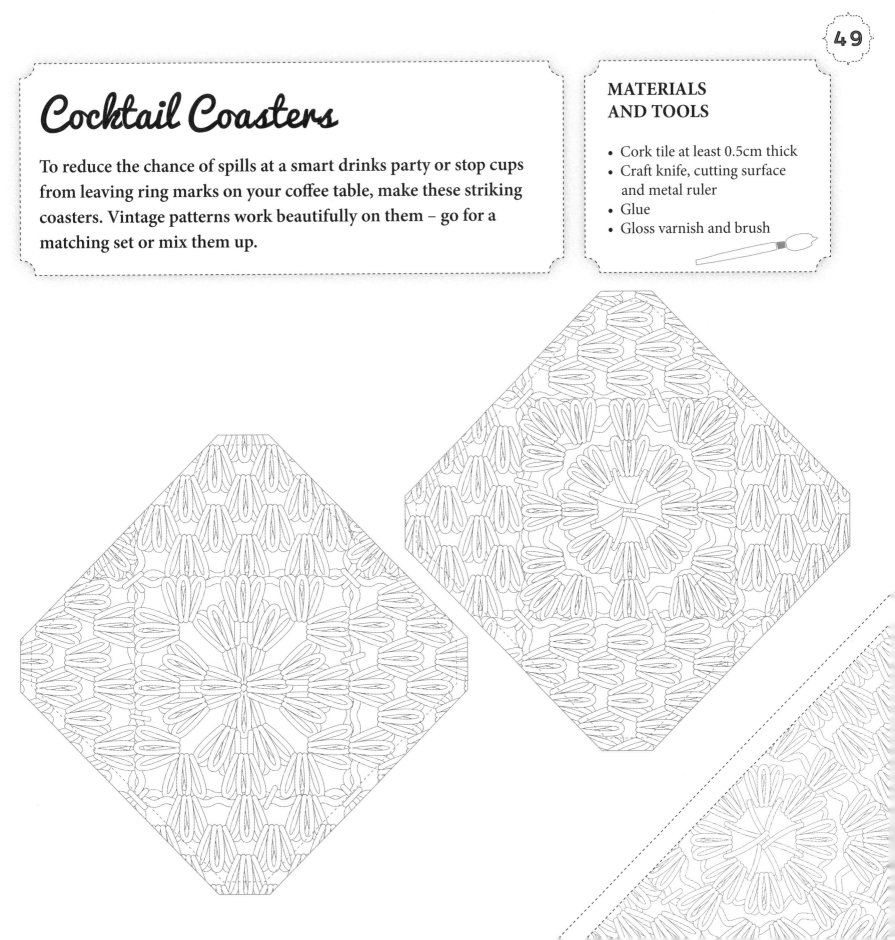

INSTRUCTIONS

1 To make a set of four coasters, choose your designs, colour them in – you only need to colour one side – and cut them out.

2 Using one of the designs as a template, draw round it on the cork. Rest the cork on the cutting surface and cut it out with the craft knife. Repeat this three times.

3 Glue the designs to the cork backing, smooth out any wrinkles and let the glue dry.

4 Give the coasters at least three coats of varnish – the more, the better. Let the varnish dry between coats, be careful not to seal in any dust and sand lightly between coats if there are any lumps or bumps.

5 If you don't have cork tile, you can use the cork from an old noticeboard or back the coasters with thick cardboard and add a layer of felt to the bottom to stop them from slipping.

MORE IDEAS AND INFORMATION

• A set of coasters tied up with pretty ribbon makes a lovely gift.

• Use the same technique to make placemats.

• If you don't have any varnish, you can seal the coasters with several layers of PVA glue. They will still look great, but may not be quite so durable.

Notebook Cover

Customise a notebook to give to someone else or keep for yourself – you could jot down craft ideas in it. This project features an elastic closure band and uses a small notebook, but it can be adapted for any size.

MATERIALS AND TOOLS

- Notebook no larger than 12cm x 15cm
- Double-sided sticky tape and glue
- Craft knife and cutting surface
- 30cm of 1cm coloured elastic

INSTRUCTIONS

1 Colour in the two cover and two spine parts – you only need to colour one side. Cut them out.

2 Join the spine parts with tape, centre on the spine of the notebook, trim level with the notebook top and bottom and stick on, overlapping onto the front and back.

3 Using double-sided tape, stick the front cover to the notebook front so that it abuts the spine and overlaps on the other sides. Open the notebook, fold in the paper edges, cut off the corners and stick them down. Do the same for the back cover.

4 Mark the top left-hand corner of the back cover 1.5cm down and 2cm in. Mark the bottom left-hand corner of the back 1.5cm up and 2cm in. Using the cutting surface and craft knife, cut two 0.7cm-wide slots through the cover and the notebook itself.

5 Thread the elastic through the top slot to the inside and glue it in place. Run it over the top of the notebook, down the front, up the back and in through the bottom slot. There should be no slack, but it shouldn't be too tight. Trim and glue to the inside back cover.

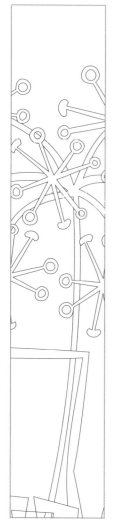

MORE IDEAS AND INFORMATION

• Adorn the front of the notebook with the owner's initials. Use the alphabet on page 91.

• For front and back endpapers, cut coloured-in designs about 1cm smaller on each side than the inside covers and glue in place.

• Instead of the elastic closure band, you could insert a ribbon tie.

Cactus

Cute. That's the only word for this mini cactus. Sit it on your desk and you'll smile every time you look at it. This taps into the trend for indoor plants yet never needs watering, although an occasional light dust wouldn't go amiss...

MATERIALS AND TOOLS

- Sticky tape
- Cocktail sticks

INSTRUCTIONS

1 Colour in the pot – you only need to colour one side of this – and both sides of the cactus shapes, plus a set of flowers or extra stem pieces, or a combination of flowers and stem.

2 Cut them all out and cut the slot lines as marked. Colour cocktail sticks with pen and tape them vertically to the cactus pieces on the less visible side.

3 Gently bend the pot shape into a circle and put the tab through the slot. You can add tape on the inside to hold it.

4 Slot the two cactus shapes together, slide the flowers or extra stem pieces into the slots on the cactus arms and place the cactus inside the pot.

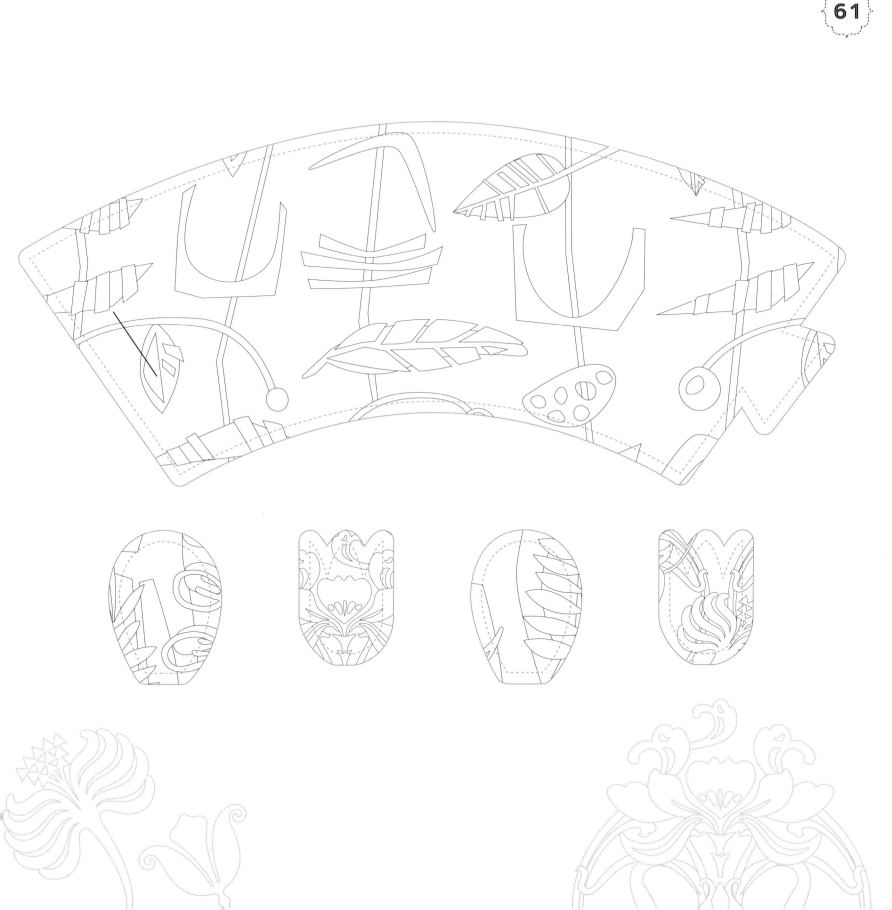

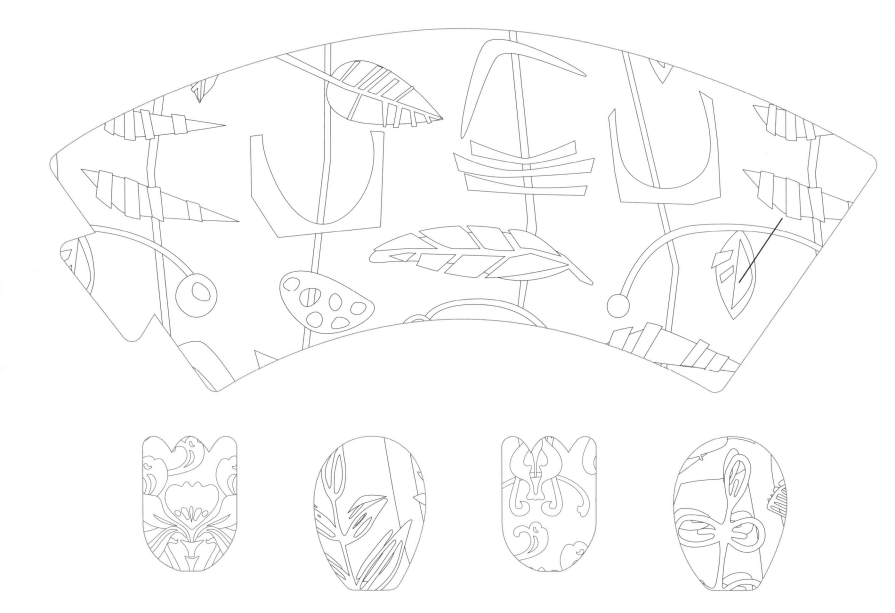

MORE IDEAS AND INFORMATION

• You don't have to stick to greens – colour your cactus any colour you want!

• For a 3D picture, layer the stems and the pot, minus the slots. Separate them with thick card and decorate with the flowers.

• If you have access to a photocopier, make another two cacti – they look great in a row.

Memory Game

This project tests your colouring-in skills as well as your memory, because each pair of cards must be identical. To confuse your opponent and make the game really hard, take one pair with the same pattern and use a different colour scheme.

MATERIALS AND TOOLS

- Medium-thick card
- Glue

INSTRUCTIONS

1 Choose a pair of cards and colour them identically - you only need colour one side. Cut them out, stick them on the card and cut them out again.

2 Repeat with the other pairs of cards, making each pair the same but different to the other pairs.

3 To play the game, place all the cards face down. Each player turns over two cards at a time. If the cards don't match, they turn them back over and memorise their position. This goes on until all the pairs have been found and a winner is declared.

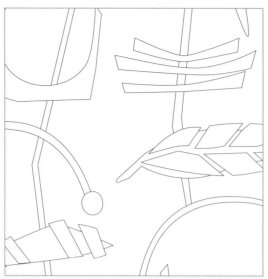
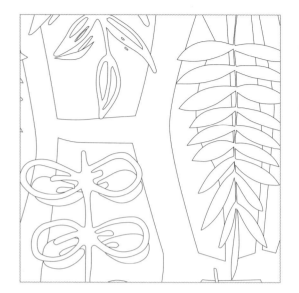

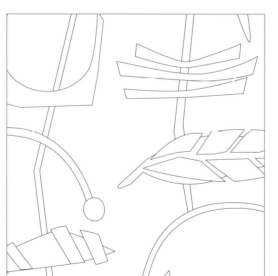

MORE IDEAS AND INFORMATION

• To give this game as a gift, back the cards with plain coloured paper, write out the instructions and box them up.

• Vintage memory game cards look fantastic in a multi-aperture frame and so would a selection of these cards.

• Their size makes these squares good for small decoupage projects.

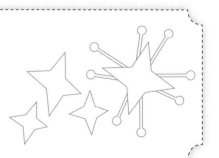

Light Holder

A candle-lit room is always lovely and yours will be even more beautiful with one of these stylish light holders, made from an empty jar. It will glow gently and uses battery-operated tealights, so it is safe in a child's bedroom, too.

MATERIALS AND TOOLS

- Straight-sided jar
- Craft knife and cutting s
- Metal ruler
- Double-sided sticky tape
- Battery-operated tealight

89

INSTRUCTIONS

1 This project is designed for use with small sauce or pickle jars about 8cm tall, with a diameter of about 5cm, but can be easily adapted for other sizes.

2 Choose a design, colour in one side and cut it out. Roll the paper round the jar.

The ends should meet or slightly overlap. Trim or add extra paper if they don't.

3 On your cutting surface, use the craft knife and metal ruler to cut around the edge of the white areas. Press them out gently.

4 Run a piece of double-sided sticky tape down the side of the jar and stick the paper round the jar.

5 If the jar doesn't have straight sides, use the top diameter for sizing, keep the paper straight and be careful not to crush the paper at the bottom.

6 Switch on a battery-operated tealight and pop it inside the jar.

MORE IDEAS AND INFORMATION

- For coloured light, stick tissue over the cut-outs on the sleeve reverse.

- To hang your light holder, twist wire tightly around the jar rim. Arc another piece from one side to the other, again twisting tightly.

- If you need a bigger sleeve, make a feature of any joins by using washi tape.

Pendant Box

Rather than letting your favourite necklace get tarnished or tangled up, pop it into one of these pendant boxes. They tuck away neatly, but will look pretty on your dressing table, too.

MATERIALS AND TOOLS

- Cutting surface
- Bone folder or blunt knife
- Metal ruler
- Glue or double-sided sticky tape
- 1cm thick foam
- Craft knife

INSTRUCTIONS

1 Colour the box. You don't need to colour the tab on the outside or the base on the inside. Cut it out.

2 On the cutting surface, with the inside face up, score along the dotted lines with the bone folder or blunt knife. Use the metal ruler for straight edges. Gently bend along the scored lines and fold the sides in towards the centre.

3 Run glue or tape along the tab. Fold it under and bring the other side round to meet it. Press together firmly.

4 Colour the insert shape – you only need to colour one side – and cut it out. Cut a piece of foam the same size and stick the paper on top. With the craft knife, cut through the paper and foam along the marked line.

5 Feed your pendant chain through the slot, rest the pendant on the insert and slip this into the box. Close by pushing the ends in.

MORE IDEAS AND INFORMATION

• This box can be used to store other pieces of jewellery or any other small items.

• If you don't want to use the insert, colour in the inside base of the box.

• If you're using your pendant box for a gift, decorate it with one of the card toppers on page 17.

Kitchen Theme Artwork

To create this piece of original artwork, you're going to fill open shelves or an old-fashioned dresser with vintage china. The strong shapes of cups, bowls, teapots, jugs and jars filled with pattern and colour make a real impact.

MATERIALS AND TOOLS

- Coloured A4 paper
- Three strips of paper –
  1.5cm x 22cm
- Glue
- Double-sided sticky pads

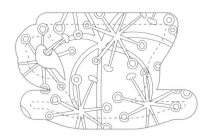

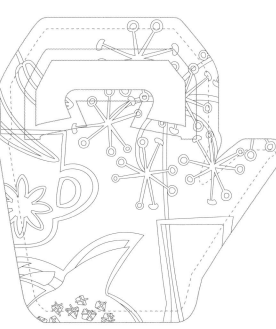

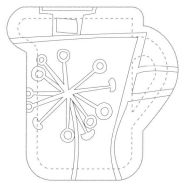

INSTRUCTIONS

1 Choose the china designs you want to use, colour them in – you only need to colour one side – and cut them out.

2 The A4 paper is the background for your artwork. It can be any colour, but should be fairly plain. Paint or colour the strips, which are the shelves, to contrast with the A4 background.

3 Stick the first strip across the bottom of the background, the second one 8.5cm above this and the third another 8.5cm above that. Trim off any excess.

4 Arrange the china shapes on the shelves, overlapping them without making it too crowded.

5 Glue on the shapes at the back first. Then add the shapes in the next layer, using two or three double-sided sticky pads to get the right 3D effect.

Finally, add the front pieces, using the sticky pads again.

6 Mount the picture on a box canvas, so that it stands out from the wall, or just tack it up with washi tape.

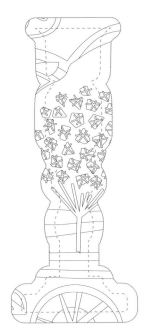
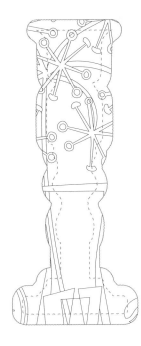

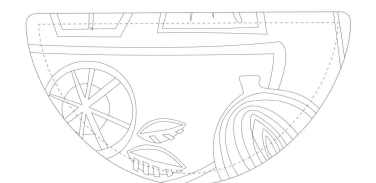
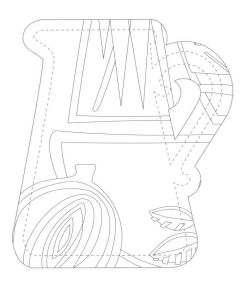

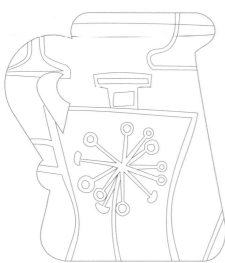

MORE IDEAS AND INFORMATION

- This paper crockery is ideal for decorating a recipe binder.

- It would also be a good way to liven up a noticeboard in a kitchen/diner.

- For a unique kitchen feature, mount the china shapes on the wall and cover them with toughened glass that's suitable for splashbacks.

3D Heart Picture

The heart is an enduring symbol. Not only does it represent love in its many different forms, it's also a rather nice, pleasing shape. This beautifully simple picture, which is enjoyable to colour and easy to craft, is an expression of all that.

MATERIALS AND TOOLS

- Backing paper or card in a plain colour
- Glue or double-sided sticky tape

INSTRUCTIONS

1 Colour the front of the first half-heart, but not the tab, and cut it out.

2 Colour the front and back of the other three half-hearts, but not the tabs, and cut them out.

3 Colour the front and half the back of the whole heart, and cut it out.

4 Position the first half-heart on the backing paper and stick it down.

5 Take the next half-heart and make a crease along the tab line. Stick the tab over the top of the tab of the first half-heart. Do the same with the remaining two half-hearts, so they are stacked on top of each other.

6 Take the whole heart and fold it in half. Position the left half over the half-hearts and stick the right half over the tabs and onto the backing paper.

7 Gently separate the halves so that they stand proud of the backing paper.

MORE IDEAS AND INFORMATION

- You could make small versions of these hearts in plain paper to position around the large heart.

- This picture works well in a box frame or hung on nails with bulldog clips.

- The technique can be adapted for any symmetrical shape – for example, a butterfly.

Home Sweet Home Picture

It's a phrase that has appeared on embroidered samplers through the ages and here is an updated version for colouring in. There's no place like home – and there will be no place like your home when this unique artwork is hanging in it.

MATERIALS AND TOOLS

- A4 backing paper or card
- Glue or double-sided sticky tape

INSTRUCTIONS

1 Colour each block, making sure you choose colours that make the words stand out, and cut them out.

2 Assemble them on the backing paper and stick them down.

MORE IDEAS AND INFORMATION

• For an extra embellishment, run strips of patterned washi tape across the top, bottom and where the blocks join.

• Mounting the picture on a piece of strongly coloured A3 card will make it really stand out.

• Use the alphabet on page 91 to send a different message.

Christmas Baubles

If 'tis the season to be jolly, deck the halls with these easy-to-make Christmas baubles. If you really want your tree to shine, use metallic pens and hang your baubles with gold ribbon.

MATERIALS AND TOOLS

- Glue
- Needle and cotton thread or stapler
- Florist wire or similar

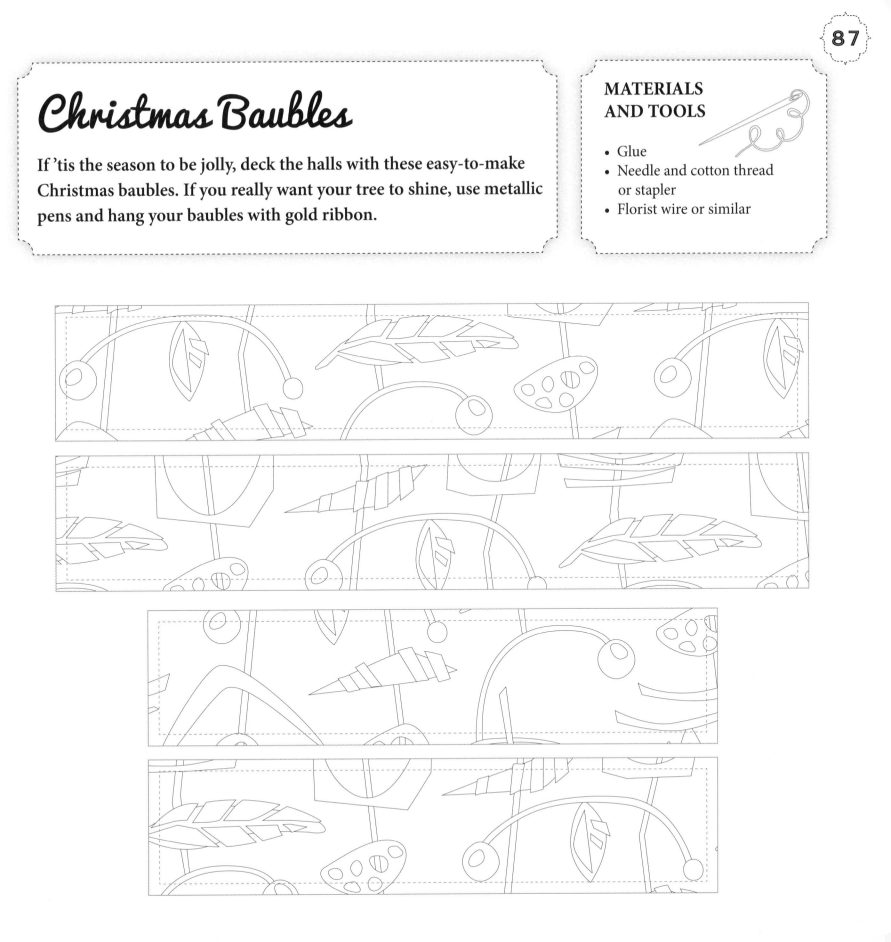

INSTRUCTIONS

1 To make the first bauble, colour the strips and cut them out. Stack the strips in this order: long, medium, short, medium, long.

2 With the needle and thread, sew all the strips together at one short end and leave

a loop for hanging the bauble. If you're in a hurry, you can staple them and slip the hanging thread under the staple.

3 Gather together the other ends of the strips and sew them together. The outer

strips will bulge out, while the central strip will remain straight.

4 To make the second bauble, colour the shapes and cut them out.

5 Make the cuts as marked and slot the two parts together.

6 Use the needle and thread to create a loop for hanging.

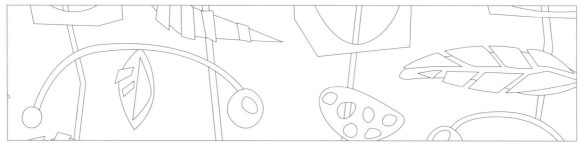

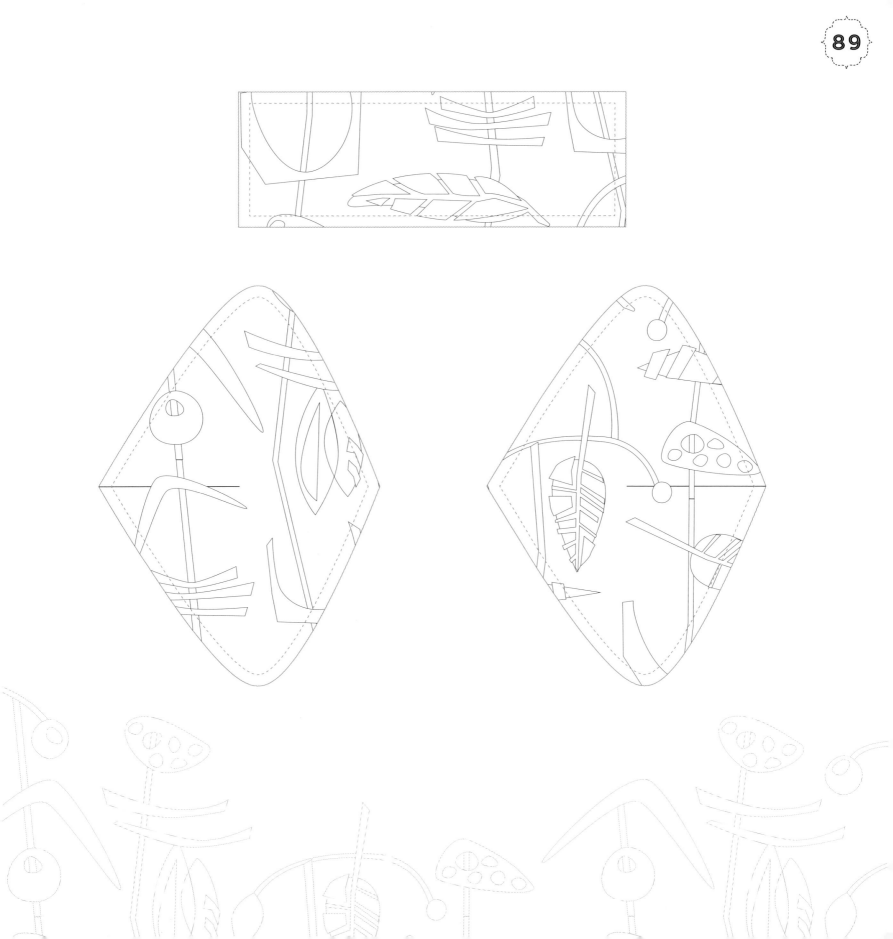

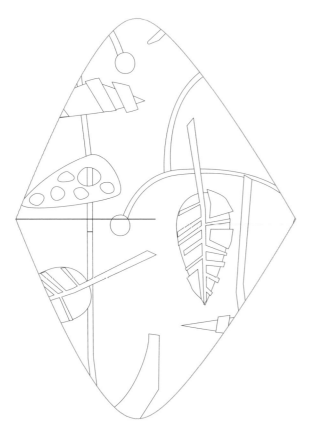

MORE IDEAS AND INFORMATION

• Choose seasonal red and green or go wild and break with tradition – neons would be fabulous.

• Bling up a window treatment by adding glitter highlights and stringing your decorations on a strand of tinsel.

• Baubles aren't just for Christmas. Hang these from a branch and they'll look effective all year round.

Vintage Alphabet

These letters are an incredibly useful resource for your crafting. Personalise a picture or product with an initial or a name, or spell out a complete phrase. All you need to do is colour them and cut them out.

MORE IDEAS AND INFORMATION

• Use the letters for a banner that proclaims 'Happy birthday' or 'Welcome home'.

• Mount initials on card and hang them above a row of coat hooks – one for each member of the household.

• Make a 'Do not disturb' or 'Keep out' sign for a teenager's bedroom door.

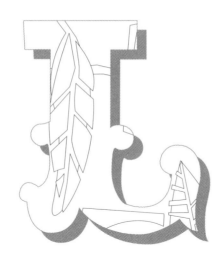

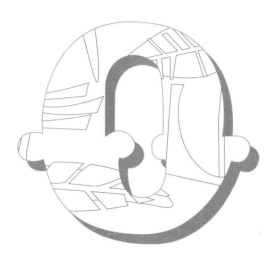

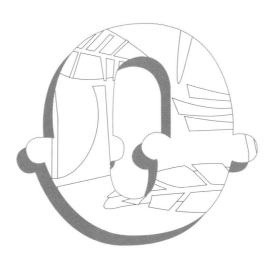

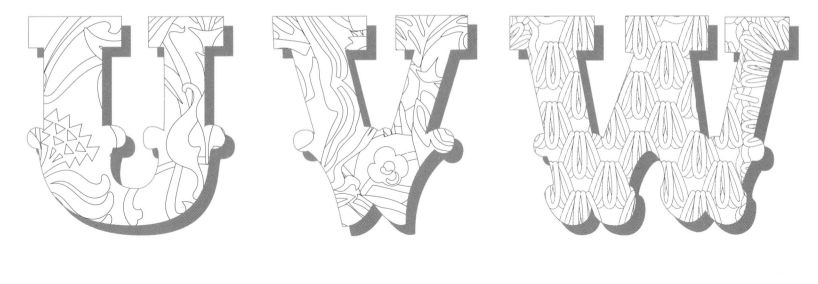